UNDERSTANDING VOICES

coping with auditory hallucinations
and
confusing realities

Marius Romme

PUBLISHED BY HANDSELL PUBLISHING 2000
ALL RIGHTS RESERVED

HANDSELL PUBLISHING
32 FURLONG ROAD
GLOUCESTER
GL1 4UT

First Published in Holland August 1996
Reprinted by Handsell Publishing 1998
Rijksuniversiteit Maastricht, Limburg, Holland
Department of Psychiatry and Neuropsychology
Section of Social Psychiatry and Psychiatric Epidemiology
Editor Prof. Dr. M. A. J. Romme

CONTENTS

UNDERSTANDING VOICES

Introduction

Marius Romme

In this booklet we will report on our experiments and studies concerning people who hear voices with the characteristics of auditory hallucinations, by reproducing three articles giving an overview of our research.

The first study was published in the Schizophrenia Bulletin (1989), reporting an experiment in which people with auditory hallucinations were brought into contact with each other. They all heard voices and described their experiences to each other. They also filled out a questionnaire about their experiences.

We then realized that auditory hallucinations, is apparent with different patients as well as with non-patients. The characteristics of a persons auditory hallucination also showed to be non-specific to particular illnesses like schizophrenia; dissociative disorders; manic depressive psychoses etc.

The second paper was held on a conference organized by the department of psychology at the University of Liverpool in 1992 and published in 1996 by Haddock and Slade in a book 'Cognitive interventions with psychotic disorders', focusing on different symptoms, mainly on auditory hallucinations. Our paper Chapter 8 covered a pilot study comparing people who heard voices either diagnosed as schizophrenic, or as having an affective disorder. We described in this chapter our case studies in which we were able to relate the experience of hearing voices experience with the person's life history experiences. We concluded that hearing voices is not primarily an incomprehensible symptom of an illness but more a personal way of coping with personal problems

The last article in this booklet is translated into English and was originally published in a Belgium book 'De wereld van schizofrenie' (in Dutch). This chapter describes the main results of our comparative study of three groups with auditory hallucinations. In this more extensive research we systematically compared two patient groups, one diagnosed with schizophrenia and one with a dissociative disorder. These two groups were compared with each other and with a third group who heard voices but had not become a psychiatric patients. We call them the non-patient group. We did this study in order to see if our previous results could be repeated or not. Our main interests were as follows:

- Do the formal criteria of auditory hallucinations differ between the three groups. Are the Schneiderian criteria for instance specific to schizophrenia?
- Is there a difference in the effect of the voices on the person who hears them between the three groups. Are there differences in the involvement with the voices?
- Are there differences in the relationship between the voices and the life history. For instance does a dissociative disorder relates to traumatic event? Is this also the case in schizophrenia? What about the non-patients?

This study will also be reported in more detail in an English book that we expect to publish next year.

In this booklet we enclose a small chapter describing the main results of our studies about the possibility to prevent psychotic decompensation in patients with auditory hallucinations.

We include the semi-structured interview we developed. This interview enables a dialogue with a person with auditory hallucinations about their voices, organized so that the information can be used to analyze the relationship between the experience of hearing voices and the life history. This booklet ends with a list of our main publications.

VOL. 15, NO. 2, 1989   SCHIZOPHRENIA BULLETIN

HEARING VOICES

Marius A.J. Romme and
Alexandre D.M.A.C. Escher

HEARING VOICES

Marius A.J. Romme and

Alexandre D.M.A.C. Escher

Abstract

An experiment is described in which people with auditory hallucinations were brought into contact with each other. On an evening television talk show, a patient, diagnosed several times as having schizophrenia, talked about her voices. Four hundred and fifty people who also were hearing voices reacted to the program by telephone. A questionnaire was sent to those who responded to the television program in order to get more information about their way of coping with the voices. From those who filled out the questionnaire, 20 people were selected who explained their experiences in a clear way. A meeting for people hearing voices was organized, and the 20 persons were invited to become the speakers. In this article the experiences described by the participants are reported as well as the many ways in which they coped with these experiences.

For some years, one of my patients, a 30 year old woman, has heard voices in her mind. These voices give her orders or forbid her to do things. They dominate her completely. She has been hospitalized several times and diagnosed as having schizophrenia. Neuroleptics do not have any effect on the voices, although they reduce the anxiety provoked by them. But the medication also reduces her mental alertness. For that reason, in order to stay alert, my patient does not take medication over long periods and does not remain an inpatient long when she is hospitalized. Nevertheless, the voices isolated her more and more by forbidding her to do things she always loved to do.

Last year she started to talk increasingly about suicide. I felt she was taking a road with no turning point. The only positive topic in our communication then was the theory she developed about the phenomenon of the voices. The theory was based on a book written by the American psychologist Julian Jaynes (1976), *The Origin of Consciousness in the Breakdown of the Bicameral Mind.* It was reassuring for her that the author described hearing voices as having been a normal way of making decisions until about 1300 B.C. According to Jaynes, hearing voices has disappeared and replaced by what we now call "consciousness".

I began to wonder if she could communicate especially effectively with others who also heard voices, and whether her theory would be accepted by other people who had these experiences. This might have a positive effect on her isolation, her suicidal tendency, and her feeling dependent on the voices. She and I began to plan together how she might share some of her experiences and views.

From this point, things progressed rapidly. Speaking on a popular Dutch television program, my patient and I invited people to contact us. After the television program, 700 persons responded to our appeal; 450 of them heard voices. Of these 450, 300 reported not being able to cope with the voices and 150 said they were able to handle them. Hearing from this last group was especially important in encouraging me to organize a congress for people who heard voices and who wanted to exchange ideas about their experiences.

We sent out a questionnaire to those who responded to the television program in order to get more information from them. From those who returned the questionnaire, we selected a number of people who could cope with the voices and invited them for an interview about their way of coping. We selected 20 persons who we thought were able to explain their experiences in a clear way and who would like to tell their experiences to others who could not handle their voices. These 20 became the speakers at a congress attended by 300 people who heard voices, a congress that took place on October 13, 1987.

The congress itself was held in a large labour union meeting building not connected physically or administratively to any psychiatric or even medical institution. Although members of the psychiatry department were active in organizing and guiding the meeting, the plenary speakers were all people who had responded to the television program and heard voices. Following the morning plenary session, there was a series of 1-hour smaller group workshops with facilitators from the department of psychiatry who did not lead the discussions but rather guided them or helped out as necessary.

The general atmosphere of the entire congress was of a meeting of a group of people with common interests and experiences. Although medical aspects of these experiences were discussed, there was no sense that this was a medical meeting or a meeting of medical patients. The participants shared freely their experiences, their many interpretations of these experiences including religious views or a range of other human reactions, and their approaches to coping. Some people were obviously troubled by their voices and saw them as part of a mental illness, but many had very different ways of understanding these experiences and appeared to be competent, not disabled, and depending on one's view of the nature of voices, not in any way "ill".

The considerable range of experiences described by the participants and the many ways they dealt with these experiences, successfully or unsuccessfully, can be viewed from many perspectives. It seems most useful to divide the reports into three possible *phases* they reflected relevant to coping with the voices:
• The startling phase: the usually sudden onset, primarily as a frighten-

ing experience.
- The phase of organization: the process of selection and communication with the voices.
- The stabilization phase: the period in which a more continuous way of handling the voices is acquired.

Many participants described phases of roughly this type. For example, one of the speakers distinguished the following phases in the process of learning to cope with the voices: (1) fear, anxiety and escape; (2) investigation of what the voices mean and accepting the voices as independent beings; and (3) accepting myself, exploring what I try to escape from, reversing the confrontation with the voices, and not trying to escape any more.

In this report, we illustrate the three phases found among people who learned to handle their voices. We also present information from the questionnaire about the frequency of experiences and coping mechanisms described.

The Startling Phase

Most people who heard voices said that it began quite suddenly, at a moment they well remembered. This was usually a startling and anxiety-provoking experience.

> On a Sunday morning at ten o'clock, it suddenly was as if I received a totally unexpected enormous blow on my head. I was alone and there was a message - a message at which even the dogs would turn up their noses. I instantly panicked and couldn't prevent terrible events from happening. My first reaction was: What on earth is happening? The second was: I'm probably just imagining things. Then I thought: No, you're not imagining it, you have to take this seriously.

The age of onset for the initial experience of voices varied widely. Many of the respondents stated that their voices had started in childhood. For 6 percent of the questionnaire respondents, onset occurred before age 6; for 10 percent, onset was between ages 10 and 20. One of the speakers told about her first experience as a child.

> As long as I remember I have had one, and later more voices inside myself. My earliest memories about voices go back to kindergarten. Perhaps it sounds funny but I had two "egos". A normal child-ego, fitting with my age, and an adult-ego. The voice adapted itself to the ego. It spoke a child-language to the child and an adult-language to the other ego. The adult-ego gradually disappeared in primary school. As a

child, I didn't experience these two egos as strange.
In fact, for a child, nothing is strange.

A representative of those who started hearing the voices in their adolescence, in a period of developing personal independence, told us:

In 1977, after high school, I decided to move into
lodgings. I must say student life was fascinating, but
I didn't sleep enough; I didn't eat regularly. After 4
months, I wanted to paint the large white wall in my
room. That wall was challenging me. Painting is like
bringing something from your head to your hands. I
started to paint a dark forest on the wall, with a rep-
tile on the foreground. I have always been able to
hear colours. They transmit vibrations. I can hear
black, red, and deep brown. During the painting it
was deathly quiet in the room. The radio wasn't on.
In this silence, something frightening was slowly
growing. Something threatening was coming up. I
had the feeling I wasn't alone in the room any more.
Then I heard a monotonous sound in my ears that
didn't come from myself and which I couldn't explain. It was a bit like the squeaking you hear when
your ears are closed, only this sound was lower and
more monotonuous. It was like an emotion, but
deeper. I had the feeling something was looking for
me.

Antecedents to the Voices' Initial Occurrence
To the question whether the onset of the voices was due to a certain event,
70 percent of the respondents answered that the voices began after a traumatic (traumatic = emotional) event, such as accident (4 percent), divorce
or death (14 percent), a psychotherapy session (12 percent), spiritism (4
percent), other events like illness, being in love, moving or pregnancy (36
percent).

Impact of the Voices
People who began to hear voices after a trauma described two general
impacts. The first was that the voices were helpful, the beginning of an
integrative coping process. They evoked a feeling of recognition or marked
a period of rest after a miserable time. Afterwards, these people felt the
purpose of the voices was to strengthen them, for example, or to raise
their self-esteem. The voices were viewed positively, and as understandable aspects of their internal selves.

For other respondents, the voices were considered as aggressive
and negative from the beginning. One woman said: "The positive voices
were suddenly accompanied by what I call real crooks, who could be-

come very nasty," and "They came from everywhere: in my head, behind me, in front of me. It seemed like if telephone lines operated from inside my chest." Among these individuals, the voices were hostile, and were not generally accepted as parts of the self or as internally generated phenomena.

People who considered the voices as negative often perceived them to be causing chaos in their minds, and demanding so much attention that the people could hardly communicate with the outside world anymore. One man reported:

> In no time (through the voices) I made contact with family members, friends, neighbours, colleagues, the psychiatrist, the police, secret service, criminals, politicians, members of the royal family and other well-known people. I got in touch with plants, animals, and things. I even discovered 'robot people'. Once, my brother came to visit me and his eyes were a bit glassy, his skin was smooth. I thought he had been replaced by a robot. I had to take care, because robots are awfully strong. I talked to him in a superficial way and got rid of him as soon as possible.

The Phase of Organization: Coping with the voices
Many people who heard voices got confused by them and wanted to escape. For some of these people, the period of hearing voices only lasted weeks or months. For others, this period lasted many years. From the interviews, it emerged that after the panic and the feeling of powerlessness, there was a period of great anger towards the voices. This anger, however, did not seem to be a fruitful coping strategy. Mr. R. told us:

> Every time I thought I had telepathic contact with people, I went to visit them. If those people denied having telepathic contact with me, then I argued with the voices. So we scolded each other; there was a lot of negative communication. This only made the voices stronger and more aggressive.

Ignoring the voices was another strategy employed by those with unfriendly voices. From the questionnaire it appeared that only 33 percent of the respondents were able to ignore the voices successfully. This strategy did not always seem a good solution. The effort spent on ignoring often led to a curtailment in the scope of activities, as noted in the following description:

> Finally I decided to ignore the voices and asked them to leave me along. In all my ignorance I handled this in a totally wrong way. You can't just put aside something that is existing in yourself and manifesting in

such a strong way. Moreover, the result of such a decision would be that the voices would lose their right to exist because of a lack of attention and energy, and of course this was not what they wanted. Until then the voices had always been polite and friendly, but it changed in the opposite way: they said all kinds of strange things and they made the things that were important to me look ridiculous. It was a full-blown civil war, but I was determined to win and I continued to ignore everything. And I did so by keeping myself busy the entire day. In that period, I solved a lot of crossword puzzles, my house had never been cleaner and the allotment garden was never taken care of better. The result was that life became more peaceful, but in a constrained way; I almost couldn't relax anymore.

The most fruitful strategies, described by people who heard voices, was to select the positive voices and listen and talk only to them, trying to understand them.

The woman who had talked about ignoring the voices said:

In this period of ignoring the voices, to my surprise there were two voices that wanted to help me. My first reaction was to send them away, because this whole story was getting on my nerves, but they insisted that I needed them and to be honest, I realized this was true. The voices taught me how to watch, hear, and feel. For example, they asked me: "How do you hear us and in what way do we talk to you?" And I, very smart, answered: "Well, I just hear you with my ears, and you talk with your mouth". "Oh really", was the answer, "then where is our larynx and in the same time we would like you to notice how you answer us". I was very much amused by this last remark. At first I took everything literally which didn't improve the already strained relation with the voices. We then agreed to say everything twice, at least the important things: once as we always did, and the second time in symbols in an expressive way. The receiver would repeat briefly the essence of what was expressed. At first we jerked along. I wasn't used at thinking in symbols at all, but I could immediately apply what they taught me and as a result I began to feel better.

Accepting the voices seemed to be related to a process of growth toward taking responsibility for one's own decisions. Others cannot always be blamed for problems. Or as some people described it, you have to learn to think in a positive way about yourself, the voices, and your own problems.

Another strategy that was frequently mentioned was "drawing limits" or "structuring the contact," whether or not accompanied by ritual or repeated acts. An example was given by someone who heard negative voices and interpreted them as follows:

> I must mention that I was attacked by the evil. With my ego-will, I choose not to be identified with the evil. The evil in myself, the evil in others, the evil in things surrounding me - I don't want it to be there. That's why I make gestures. You can also do that in your mind. I think you really turn your back to the voices, only by making a physical gesture. "This doesn't fit me, I throw the message away". That gives me a feeling of relief, and then I think: "There, good riddance to bad rubbish." Next, I send away the messenger, and I say aloud or in my mind "You just go to your friends, don't bother me with this". That is the first step. The second step is choosing with my own will to make contact - to associate with the light in me, the most beautiful thing there is. I have a source of heat and a healthy core, consisting of pure healthy energy. I know such a thing is present in each human being and that we can choose whether to make contact or not.

In the preceding section, two dimensions of relating to voices emerge: (1) The friendliness or hostility felt, and (2) the relationship or location of the voice relative to the "host" or person hearing the voice. Some respondents integrated the voices as accepted, hostile foes. There is, however, no simple association between internality, friendliness, and acceptance or hostility, externality, and attempts to reject, ignore, or control the voices. In the next section, we heard more about coping modes that worked for the respondents and congress attendees.

Phase of Stabilization

People who learned to cope with the voices developed a kind of balance. In this stabilization the individuals saw the voices as a part of themselves. The voices are part of life and self and they can have a positive influence. In this phase, the individual is able to choose between following the advice of the voices or his or her own ideas. These people are able to say: 'I hear voices, and I'm happy for that.' One woman told us:

> They show me the things I do wrong and teach me how to do them otherwise. But they leave the choice to me if I really want to change it or rather leave it as it was. They think the way I listen to music isn't right. I lose

myself in music and they think I shouldn't. I tried the
way they think I should listen to music, but I didn't
want to make the effort, I don't see the use of it. Such
a decision is taken in mutual consideration, but I have
the final choice and the voices always resign to it.

Another speaker said:
Later on, it seemed as if life was slowing down a little.
I was in calmer waters and I could concentrate on my
own life again.

A third woman described:
When you fall with your bicycle, you don't throw it
away, but you continue in the right relation to each
other. You create a beautiful bicycle trip just as it can
go in your inner self. Finally, I have the feeling to be
neither the winner nor the loser, but it is as if a dimension is added to my life, a dimension that you dare to
handle and which can be useful in the end.

Comparisons of People Who Coped Well With the Voices and Those Who Did Not

The frequency of different types of response to hearing voices and coping
in this group of people is illustrated by tabulations of the responses to the
questionnaire that had been completed prior to the congress. We arrange
these data by the differences between those persons who could cope with
the voices (group A) and those who could not (group B). In table 1 only
the variables that appeared to distinguish the two groups are listed. Many
people (33.8 percent) reported that they were able to manage their voices
well, but 66.2 percent said they could not. People who could not handle
the voices generally experienced them as negative and aggressive, whereas
people who could cope with their voices often experienced them as positive and friendly.

The process of coping is complex and entails many variations in
this preliminary sample. The common dimensions include: the attributed
meaning of the voice; the hostility or friendliness seen in the voice and its
messages; the degree of interference or rejection of the voice as internal
and part of self or external and alien; the nature of the voice as psychological, medical, spiritual, or the personification of someone else. Coping success, as discussed in the next section, appears to entail reaching
some sort of peaceful accommodation and acceptance of the voice as "part
of me". Those strategies that focused on ignoring a hostile, "not-part-of-
me" voice were less adaptive. At this early juncture in the study of voices
from the individual's perspective, we can only suggest further scrutiny of
these dimensions and their efficacy in coping strategies.

16

Frames of Reference

In the introduction we noted that the 30-year-old woman (one of our patients) who heard voices was somewhat reassured by adopting a specific frame of reference (Jaynes 1976). We wondered whether others would share her theory. This was a naive expectation, because it became clear that there are a great many frames of reference used by the people who heard voices. These frames of reference included psychodynamic, mystical, parapsychological, and medical perspectives. Each of these perspectives has examples in writings of many authors the congress participants had read (Jung 1961; Ehrenwald 1978; Pierrakos 1979; Roberts 1979; Atkinson 1985). In an attempt to classify the frames of reference somewhat, we used two main categories: (1) viewing the voices as a psychological phenomenon arising from within the individual (e.g., coming from mystical, psychodynamic, or parapsychologic origins), and (2) viewing the voices as a phenomenon the causes of which lie primarily outside psychological characteristics of the person.

Viewing voices as a phenomenon related to "not me" psychological characteristics within the person

This perspective, which was described by many participants has origins in many scholarly sources. Carl Jung (1961), for example, had a psychodynamically based view that impulses from the unconscious speak to humans in visions or voices. Jung's work appealed to many "voice hearers". By reading his books, they felt they developed a better understanding of their voices and what those voices were trying to tell them.

Another relevant psychodynamic theory focuses more on psychodynamic mechanisms for dealing with emotions. It is assumed that a human being may react to an extremely traumatic experience such as incest, sadistic rearing patterns, life-threatening accidents, hostageship, and acts of war by isolating these memories from the consciousness. The trauma then returns in forms of flashbacks, feeling pursued, aggressive voices, or terrifying images (Putnam 1987). Some speakers in the conference seemed to be using this strategy of interpreting their voices as coping mechanisms to deal with the emotions provoked by life events.

Mystics have an explanation for hearing voices that is not based on fear but on development (Roberts 1979). They often assume that people have the capacity to expand their consciousness by developing spirituality. Voices may be viewed as part of that expansion. By training themselves, people are able to overstep their limits in a spiritually creative, divine, and/or cosmic ego.

A third "psychological" explanation is given by parapsychology. From this perspective, voices may be viewed as originating from a special gift or sensitivity. It is even possible that a person can be a medium for others. Voices thus are understood as occurring at a more subtle sense of consciousness. The purpose of parapsychology is to handle this sensitivity, for the benefit of oneself or for others. From this perspective, one does not want to lose such a sensitivity, but rather wants to cope with it. It is important to draw limits, to learn to handle the sensitivity instead of being overrun.

Table 1. Difference between "good coping" and "bad coping" individuals

		Group A good coping (%)	Group B bad coping (%)
Nature of voices			
Mostly friendly		24	18
Friendly, aggressive or giving commands		25	17
Mostly negative		15	39
Who is stronger?			
Self		85	50
The voices		15	50
How do you cope with the voices?			
Selecting	Yes	50	15
	No	50	85
Draw limits	Yes	50	33
	No	50	67
Distraction	Yes	25	40
	No	75	60
Do you have to obey the voices?			
	Yes/sometimes	40	75
	No	60	25
Can you ignore the voices?			
	Yes	58	28
	Sometimes	6	34
	No	35	37
Are the voices disturbing the contact with others?	Yes	32	75
	No	68	25

Do the voices take over your thoughts?			
	Yes	33	47
	No	67	53
Did you learn to cope with them on your own strength?	Yes	80	30
	No	20	70
How do you interpret the voices?			
As gods or spirits	Yes	50	40
	No	50	60
As a good guide	Yes	25	14
	No	75	86
As people you know	Yes	15	35
	No	85	65
As a special gift	Yes	46	22
	No	54	78

Views about voices as caused by factors not primarily psychological in origin or external to the person

One group of other than psychological explanations described by participants is founded biologically oriented psychiatry. Voices are viewed as a symptom of an illness, believed to be anchored in the biological functioning of the brain. Several participants at the congress held this view. For example, one person said:

> I never experienced the voices as something from outside myself, I know they are inside of me and I can do something about it. I take medication on a daily basis, and I know I will have to do so for the rest of my life. However, this doesn't bother me. I have been working for 10 years as a secretary and I feel good.

Another very different group of nonpsychological explanations is presented more broadly by the Society for Natural Medicine, a group interpreting voices as spirits of wandering deceased. Some religious groups, such as Jehovah's Witnesses, consider voices as demons. For example one person said:

> I heard three to five different voices. They were sexless and they were always threatening. I had to do exactly what they said. One day they even commanded me to kill my stepfather and at the last moment I came back to myself. Shortly after I admitted myself to a

psychiatric hospital. I got medication, but the voices remained. By means of my hobby, which is art and history of the Middle Ages, I started reading the bible. In my opinion in the bible Jesus heals people like myself. It is the story of the possessed man. Matthew VIII, verses 1-5 and Mark V, versus 2-20.

Both frames of reference described above lead to certain coping strategies logically associated with the theoretical explanations:
Group 1 includes the following:
- Psychodynamics - psychotherapy focusing on archetypes and split off emotions.
- Mysticisms - mystical training (e.g., through meditation and transcendent experiences).
- Parapsychology - learning how to deal with different levels of consciousness, keeping one's sensitivity under control.

Group 2 includes the following:
- Biological psychiatry - medication.
- Natural medicine - escort of the wandering deceased.
- Religion - faith healing.

If coping attempts are to be made, it seems very important for individuals to adopt a frame of reference, to attribute some meaning of the voice; otherwise it is very difficult to start the phase of organizing one's relationship to the voices to reduce anxiety. Interestingly, at least in terms of coping efforts, it seems unfortunate when individuals adopt a frame of reference discouraging them from attempting to master the voices. Viewing the voices as linked to electronic influences is one such example. The explanation offered by biological psychiatry may also not be very helpful in coping with the voices because it, too, places the phenomenon beyond one's grasp.

The Psychiatric Paradigm and Treatment
One hypothesis that might be generated from this congress is that the reduction of "hearing voices" to being viewed merely as a pathological phenomenon is not very fruitful in helping patients to deal with these experiences. It may also be inaccurate. Outside the world of psychiatry (Ehrenwald 1978), many people hear voices and are quite able to handle them, even experiencing the voices as enriching their lives. Thus, in the mental health professions, it may be worthwhile to explore in greater detail which frames of reference and coping strategies are best for patients who hear voices so that we can help them more effectively in learning to deal with these experiences. The main steps in this process are:
- To accept the patient's experience of the voices. Those voices are often more penetrating than sensory perceptions.

- To try to understand the different language patients use to describe their frame of reference as well as the different language the voices use for communication.
  Often a world of symbols and feelings is involved. For example, the voices might speak about light and dark when expressing love and aggression.
- To consider helping the individual communicate with the voices. Issues of differentiating good and bad voices and accepting the person's own negative emotions may be involved. Such acceptance may be assisted when support is given to promote self-esteem.
- To stimulate the patient to meet other people with similar experiences and to read about hearing voices in order to diminish the taboo and the isolation.

For most psychiatrists, these steps will require an enlargement of one's perspective in addition to broadening the generally accepted theories within the profession. We are very interested in hearing from others about the experiences they have encountered that might relate to the suggestions we received from the congress participants described above.

References

Atkinson, J.M. *Schizophrenia: A Guide for Sufferers and Their Families.*
Wellingborough: Turnstone Press, 1985.

Ehrenwald, J. *The ESP experience.*
New York: Basic Books, 1978.

Jaynes, J. *The Origin of Consciousness in the Breakdown of the Bicameral Mind.*
Boston: Houghton Mifflin, 1976.

Jung, C. *Memories, Dreams, Reflections.*
New York: Pantheon Books, Random House, 1961.

Pierrakos, E. *The Path*
New York: Phoenicia, 1979.

Putnam, F. "Dissociation as a Response to Extreme Trauma Diagnostic Workshop." Presented at a diagnostic workshop, Free University, Amsterdam, 1987.

Roberts, J. *Seth Speaks. The Eternal Validity of the Soul.*
Englewood Cliffs, NJ: Prentice Hall, 1979.

First published in: Gilian Haddock and Peter Slade 'Cognitive Behavioural, Interventions with Psychotic Disorders', Chapter 8. page 137-150, Routledge London.

Empowering people who hear voices

Marius Romme and Sandra Escher

Empowering people
who hear voices

Marius Romme and Sandra Escher

Introduction

In this chapter we intend to show that people hear voices in the normal population even when there is no evidence of psychiatric disease (Tien, 1991; Eaton *et al.*, 1991) and that the reported presence of verbal hallucinations is not always related to psychopathology (Barret and Etheridge, 1992).

Despite this, hearing voices does occur in specific psychiatric diseases at a much higher percentage than in the normal population. For example, schizophrenia, 53 per cent (Landmark *et al.*, 1990), major affective disorders, 28 per cent (Goodwin and Jamison, 1990) and the normal population, 2.3 per cent (Tien, 1991). Although these two kinds of information appear to be contradictory, there are two possible connections. First, it may be that there is a connection between specific characteristics of hearing voices and the existence of psychiatric illness, or second there may be a connection between hearing voices and problems in the person's life history. In the latter case, it is possible that psychiatric patients may have experienced more problems which they have found difficult to cope with than the average person.

In our own research, we have not found a connection between the characteristics of hearing voices and specific psychiatric illnesses. This led us to question whether hearing voices has a functional role in aiding coping with problems in daily life. In more dramatic terms: is it a survival strategy instead of a symptom of a particular illness? If this is the case, then there should be a connection between hearing voices, life history and living circumstances. To investigate this question further we conducted an experiment where we brought together a large number of people who heard voices. Within this group of voice hearers we compared people who could cope well with their voices with those who felt they could not cope.

The results of this investigation will be presented in this chapter, followed by some short case examples. These examples will demonstrate how the connection between hearing voices, life history and living circumstances manifests itself and how this connection may be handled in learning to cope with hearing voices. These examples may also demonstrate that as long as the phenomenon of hearing voices is viewed as a symptom of a disease, and treatment is focused on this disease, problems in daily life and circumstances as expressed by the voices, will not be solved.

Hearing voices in the normal population

At the end of the last century, Sidgewick (1894) showed that the phenomenon of hearing voices appeared in 2 per cent of the normal population. Recently, Tien (1991) replicated this research, with the help of the National Institute of Mental Health Epidemiological (NIMH) catchment area programme using the structured Diagnostic Interview Schedule for auditory hallucinations (D.I.S.; Robins *et al.,* 1981). He found that there was a prevalence rate of 2.3 per cent, in a survey compiled from 15,000 members of the general population. Only one third of these hallucinators reported distress or impairment of functioning (level 5 D.I.S., meeting the D.I.S. criteria for a psychiatric diagnosis. Eaton *et al.,* (1991) selected a sample of 810 individuals from the same NIMH programme. They found a prevalence rate of auditory hallucinations of 4 per cent elicited by psychiatrists using the same D.I.S. Only a small minority of these people (16 per cent) met the D.I.S. criteria for a psychiatric diagnosis.

In the 1980s, Posey and Losch (1983) and Bentall and Slade (1985) developed a questionnaire assessing different aspects of experiencing auditory hallucinations. In both studies the authors found a number of normal students who claimed to have had hallucinatory experiences. More recently, Barret and Etheridge (1992) replicated Posey and Losch's (1983) study using their auditory hallucination questionnaire, and found the same frequencies as those reported by Posey and Losch on all listed items. Subsequently, they conducted a second study where they compared hallucinators and non-hallucinators on tendencies towards psychopathology. They used the Minnesota Multiphasic Personality Inventory (M.M.P.I.) for the ten standard clinical scales (Graham, 1987). They found as many people in the hallucinating group as in the non-hallucinating group with a scale score above seventy which Graham suggests indicates pathology. This result indicates that hearing voices cannot reasonably be explained only as the result of psychopathology.

Hearing voices in psychiatric illness

If hearing voices in itself is not the result of psychopathology, then we may expect that it would not be linked to a specific disease and would appear in a wide variety of psychiatric disorders and that the quality of the voices would not be related to specific diagnoses. In order to research this particular point, the authors made an inventory of a group of patients undergoing treatment at a community health center in Maastricht, Holland. All patients were asked by their case manager (this being in most cases a Community Psychiatric nurse) to complete a questionnaire that included both open and closed questions that probed for experiences of hallucinations.

The total sample consisted of 288 patients of which 165 (57 per cent) were female. The mean age of the participants was 45 years (plus or minus 13 years), with a median age of 43 years. About one third of the population was diagnosed as having an affective disorder, one fifth with schizophrenia and the third largest diagnostic group was a personality disorder (see Table 8.1).

Twenty-eight per cent (n=81) of the population reported hearing voices over a prolonged period of time. The percentage found for the two major diagnostic groups, 53 per cent in schizophrenia and 28 per cent in affective disorders, were similar to those found by others (Landmark *et al.*, 1990; Goodwin and Jamison, 1990).

In this study, we also compared the quality of perceived hallucinations as related to these two major diagnostic groups. As Table 8.2 indicates,

Table 8.1. Auditory hallucinations per principal diagnosis in the total sample

	Total N	*no. of subjects who heard voices*	%
Total population	288	81	28
schizophrenia	62	33	53
affective disorder	90	25	28
dissociative disorder	5	4	80
psychotic disorder (N.A.O.)	17	7	41
personality disorder	48	6	13
other diagnosis	66	6	9

Table 8.2. A comparison of the quality of the voices between schizofrenia and affective disorder

Quality of the voices	*Schizophrenia*		*Affective disorders*	
	N	%	N	%
via ears	24	80	16	70
in the head	19	63	15	65
in the body	3	11	1	4
outside the head	15	52	9	39
communicate with	14	47	8	36
from self	7	24	8	17
from outside self	28	93	18	78

there were no significant differences found between those diagnosed with schizophrenia and those with an affective disorder as far as the quality of voices was concerned.

We concluded that hearing voices is present in people with very different kinds of diagnoses and that qualitative characteristics of hallucinations are not specific to a particular psychiatric diagnosis.

Coping well and coping badly

When hearing voices in itself is not the result of psychopathology, nor is it specific in characteristics to any specific psychiatric illness, it is of interest to analyze the differences between people who can cope well with their voices and those who cannot.

In an earlier study the authors brought together a group of people who heard voices (Romme and Escher, 1989). We conducted this study because in our clinical approach we felt quite powerless in our attempts to assist people with auditory hallucinations and we did not feel able to help a number of sufferers sufficiently (a notion already reported as a result of previous research by Falloon and Talbot, 1981). Even when medication helps in diminishing anxiety or chaos, one must then continue to prescribe prophylactic medication, otherwise the voices, together with their accompanying hindrances, will in most cases reoccur. Many of our patients did not know how to cope well with their voices. As a result of these observations we looked round for a television talkshow which would be willing to help us explore the phenomenon more fully. A patient with auditory hallucinations recounted her story on this talkshow and requested that people experiencing hearing voices and who were coping well with them, telephone after the programme, as we were looking for individuals who would be able to help the patient cope better. The result was unexpected as more than 500 people hearing voices responded to our request. We followed this up by sending out a questionnaire in order to obtain more information concerning the characteristics of their voices, their medical history and most important for us, their ability to cope and the methods they used. As a result of this questionnaire we learned that there were quite a number of people who could cope well with their voices, but to our astonishment, we also received questionnaires from people hearing voices, who had never been a psychiatric patient. We were especially interested in exploring the coping methods used by these people. We decided to organize a conference so that people hearing voices could meet and exchange their experiences. This conference was held in Utrecht in 1987, and resulted in the formation of an organization for people who heard voices. This organization now has more than 1000 members. By meeting a large number of these people we have had the opportunity to interview both a number of good copers and bad copers about their voice experiences and coping methods. We would like to begin with a report on some of the data accumulated from the questionnaire comparing good and bad copers, and patients and non-patients (Romme et al., 1992).

The questionnaire comprised thirty open-ended questions and was distributed amongst 450 people suffering from chronic auditory hallucinations or hearing voices. Of the 254 replies received, 186 were able to be used for analysis. It was doubtful as to whether thirteen of these respondents were actually experiencing true hallucinations therefore these were excluded. Of the remaining 173 respondents, fifty-eight reported an ability to cope with their voices.

Differences between good and bad copers existed in what we call the power structure between the voices and the person who hears them, as well as in the coping strategies that were used. Table 8.3 compares the power structure between those who said that they were able to cope well with the voices (group A) and the group who said they were not able to cope with the voices (group B).

Table 8.3 shows that those who could cope with their voices (group A) experienced themselves as significantly stronger than the voices (72 per cent) while those who could not cope experienced the voices as being

Table 8.3 A comparison of power structure between groups A and B

	Group A coping +	Group B coping -
	58 (34%)	115 (66%)
Who is stronger?		
self	39 (72%)	40 (38%)
voice	5 (10%)	44 (42%)
otherwise	9 (16%)	20 (19%)
missing	5	11
		p<0.001
Nature of voices		
positive	16 (30%)	10 (10%)
contradictory	14 (26%)	17 (16%)
negative	23 (43%)	75 (73%)
missing	5	13
		p<0.001
Imperative hallucinations		
yes	10 (20%)	26 (24%)
no	38 (74%)	41 (38%)
sometimes	3 (6%)	41 (38%)
missing	7	7
		p<0.001

total N=173

stronger. The most important differences between the two groups were:
* Those who could not cope (B) often experienced voices which were stronger than self.
* Those who could not cope (B) often experienced voices in a negative sense.
* Those who could cope (A) experienced less imperative voices.

We also found differences between the good (A) and the bad (B) copers, in the kind of coping strategies that were used. These are illustrated in Table 8.4. Those people who did not cope well with their voices (group B) used different coping strategies to those who could cope with their voices.

We also found differences in social circumstances between patients and non-patients which are shown in Table 8.5. The main differences were:
1. Non-patients were more likely to be married than patients.
2. Non-patients experienced or perceived more support than patients.
3. Non-patients were more likely to discuss their voices with people other than patients.

Table 8.4 Coping strategies comparing copers (A) and non-copers (B)

	Total	%	Group A coping + total	%	Group B coping - total	%
Distraction						
yes	42	(24%)	10	(26%)	32	(43%)
no	72	(42%)	9	(74%)	43	(57%)
missing	59	(34%)				
						p<0.05
Ignoring						
yes	54	(31%)	31	(56%)	23	(25%)
no	57	(33%)	21	(37%)	36	(39%)
sometimes	37	(21%)	4	(7%)	33	(36%)
missing	25	(14%)				
						p<0.001
Selective listening						
yes	30	(17%)	19	(46%)	11	(14%)
no	87	(50%)	22	(53%)	65	(85%)
missing	56	(33%)				
						p<0.001

Setting limits

yes	45	(26%)	19	(48%)	25	(30%)
no	79	(46%)	20	(51%)	59	(70%)
missing	49	(28%)				

p<0.001

Table 8.5 Social interactions in patients and non-patients

	Non-patients N=70		Patients N=103	
Marital status	N=58		N=79	
single	11	(19%)	30	(38%)
married	35	(60%)	31	(39%)
divorced	11	(19%)	15	(19%)
widowed	1	(2%)	3	(4%)
Perceived support	N=70		N=96	
no	1	(2%)	47	(49%)
yes	69	(98%)	49	(51%)
Do others know about my voices?				
	No=70		N=101	
no	1	(2%)	15	(14%)
yes	69	(98%)	86	(86%)

The following summarizes the differences we observed between copers and non-copers.

People who could cope with voices:

* experienced themselves as stronger;
* experienced more positive voices;
* experienced less imperative voices;
* set more limits to the voices;
* listened selectively to the voices;
* communicated more often about their voices.

People who could not cope with voices:

* experienced themselves as weaker;
* experienced more negative voices;
* experienced more imperative voices;
* did not dare to set limits to them;
* tried to escape from the voices by using more distraction techniques.

The most relevant differences between copers and non-copers may be interpreted as relating to feeling 'stronger' not only with respect to the voices, but also with respect to their environment, i.e. feeling less threatened and more supported in the environment.

Empowering people

Receiving support and having the opportunity to talk about voices with other people appear to be associated with them being accepted by others. As a result of the conference in 1987 for people who hear voices, it became clear that all of the people who heard voices experienced problems with the societal taboo factor associated with them. It is difficult to talk about voices with others without being looked at in a strange way, so therefore empowering people who hear voices will have to take place on an individual and societal level.

Our approach addresses both levels. As a way of stimulating societal changes, we organize annual conferences, information meetings in psychiatric hospitals and conduct interviews with patients and non-patients on television and in popular magazines. In the following case studies we have outlined our approaches on an individual level.

Case studies

We have developed an interview schedule that has allowed us to explore the dynamics of the relationship between the voices and the life history of patients who hear voices. We are currently investigating this relationship more systematically in a study that includes three groups of people hearing voices: those who have a diagnosis of schizophrenia, those who have a diagnosis of dissociative disorder and those who have never received a psychiatric diagnosis, but who hear voices. The results of this comparison are not yet available. In this chapter we will provide a description of some cases to illustrate the dynamics that exist between hearing voices and the life history of the person experiencing them. The following examples illustrate different categories of life influences which we have found to be related to the onset of voices.

1. Intolerable or unsatisfying living situations
2. Recent traumas
3. Aspirations or ideals
4. Childhood trauma
5. Emotional intolerance and control

When discussing these examples, the following areas are of special interest in understanding the dynamics of the interaction between voices and the life history of the person hearing them:
* the identity of the voices
* the characteristics of their communication with the person, e.g. the way of talking, the age of voices and what they say
* what triggers the appearance or disappearance of the voices
* what important change in the individual's life was related to the onset

of hearing voices
* the characteristics of a person's upbringing and childhood including any special experiences that occurred in that period

Intolerable or unsatisfying living circumstances

A 16-year-old young woman heard a voice that said unpleasant things to her. It was a male voice who called himself Erichem. In the background she also heard other voices who wanted to help her, but these voices were not very powerful. In addition, she heard voices of relatives that had passed away. She saw them and could communicate with them. They included her grandmother, her grandfather and her uncle. Sometimes she had prophecies and sometimes she saw colored auras around people.

The young woman had a problem only with the unpleasant voice, which angered her. This voice first appeared when she was 14 having problems with her father. Her father was very concerned with her performance and wanted to control her life. The voice of Erichem treated her in the same manner as her father. Whenever she was tense the voice appeared, but when she was relaxed or, for example, working at school, the voice would disappear. The voice of Erichem spoke directly to her and also spoke about her. The voices of the family members who had passed away spoke directly to her and gave her advice or offered solutions to existing problems.

The following interpretations were made relating to her voices and life history. The identity of the voice did not mean anything to her. She could not imagine a person around it or link the voice to anyone in particular. The voice was completely identified through the characteristics of its behaviour. This was more or less the same relationship that she had towards her father. The relationship was dominated by his behaviour and did not have the characteristics of a personal relationship like the one she shared with her mother. Erichem's dialogue made her angry. This was also the case with her father, but expressing anger towards him was not possible.

The following provided the starting point for treatment, beginning with the confirmation of the good relationship with her mother, together with increasing her coping strategies towards the anger of Erichem. The mother sometimes advised her on how to cope with Erichem's behaviour, which she achieved, because the mother could cope more easily with the aggression of the father than the daughter. In the next step, it was important to establish, with the help of the mother, a more personal relationship with the father rather than a relationship based on the experiences of her upbringing.

This meant that the father also had to become more personally involved with both women. Additional steps were taken to ensure that the daughter would no longer act as an intermediary in the poor relationship between the mother and father. Direct psychodynamic interpretations did not make a lot of sense in this therapeutic approach. Looking for better ways of dealing with daily living problems was more effective and made more sense. This may be particularly important for young people in their development into adulthood.

Recent trauma

Hearing voices following the death of a loved one is not uncommon (Frantz, 1984). One usually hears the voice of that specific person. This can happen for a short period of time or, in some cases, it can linger on. This is mostly dependent upon the problems encountered during the mourning process. It is less commonly known that voices can appear following other kinds of trauma, e.g. divorce or loss of a job. The following is an example:

Monique was a 30-year-old woman who was fired from her job and felt that she had been treated in an unpleasant way. Losing her job left her with a strong feeling of helplessness. She was so ashamed about what had happened to her that this made it difficult for her to talk about it. After some time she began to notice that when she sat in a cafe, for example, she would hear people seated at the table behind her talking about her and discussing what had happened to her.

She heard people say things about her in the exact voice of the person in the cafe. She found this so threatening, that after a brief period she would leave the situation. Her reaction went further than thinking people were talking about her: she clearly heard what they said about her. The identity of the people around her did not change, only the things that they were saying and how they related to her problem.

We made the following interpretation. The identities of the voices were those of people around her. This fitted in with the trauma of losing her job. She had lost her job because people from another firm had been gossiping about her. What the voices said also fitted in with the trauma because they were talking about what had happened to her. The trauma of losing her job was the change in her life which triggered the voices.

The following intervention and strategies were utilized. A direct explanation of the relationship between the voices and the loss of her job did not help and was not accepted by Monique initially. Information was provided regarding the nature of her experiences. While participating in a self-help group she discovered that she was not the only one to have had such experiences. This opened up her interest in her voices and helped to diminish the shame she was experiencing. The main issue in therapy was then to help Monique to get up the nerve to look for a new job. The voices almost completely disappeared when she started to apply, and finally found, a new job.

Aspirations and ideals

In this category we placed those people who hear voices which are easily related to certain aspirations or ideals. Examples of this are when people use their voices to guide them when they have a difficult decision to make, and also when people strive for ideals that are not possible to achieve, e.g. denying their sexuality. Here we provide an example of somebody whose voices confront him with difficulties in attaining certain desired goals.

This man was married and 27 years old when he came to our rehabilitation department. He had started to hear voices in his head and also sometimes through his ears. The voices were men and women talking to each other. He did not recognize the voices as those of people he knew. His own thoughts were repressed by the voices so that when they were there he could not think. He wanted to get rid of the voices because they mostly consisted of critical comments. The voices mainly occurred in stressful situations. Those situations were specially related to his training for an administrative education. The voices in those situations worsened his own negative thoughts about himself. He had doubts about his possibilities to follow this education and the voices confirmed these doubts in an exaggerated way. The voices were absent when he was alone or with his wife. This was confirmed by a research method called *experience sampling* (de Vries *et al.,* 1990).

The changes in his life situation when he first heard voices were not clear. We made the following interpretation. The voices did not belong to anyone special, they had no clear identity and they destroyed his own thinking. Thus, we made the interpretation that the voices confronted him with his own doubts about his education. The voices may have been right. The voices may have been more realistic than his own ideal to proceed and finish his training successfully.

In therapy this is a difficult dilemma, because it has consequences for the person's professional life and labour possibilities. The therapist dealt with this by stimulating him to formulate his own opinion about the things the voices were telling him. It took some time before the therapist, in discussion with the man, reached the conclusion that his training was too difficult. He improved, i.e. the voices reduced in frequency, after he stopped his training course. At the same time he was offered an unpaid job as a concierge at a school, which he came to like very much. He had to give up his original aspiration, but by doing so the quality of his life was augmented.

Childhood trauma in combination with emotional control

The best known trauma after which hearing voices occurs is the experience of incest. The research of Ensink (1992), showed that 27 per cent of incest victims researched heard voices later in their lives. It was striking that this phenomenon was most likely to occur when the trauma took place before the age of 7. As there are other kinds of childhood traumas associated with hearing voices, we have chosen here to provide an example of development of voices following trauma not specifically related to incest.

A young woman began to hear voices after her fourteenth birthday. When she reached age 23, the voices began to worsen and her behaviour towards the voices began to change. From that time, she began to hear voices that read her mind. This occurred two times a week, sometimes lasted for up to eight hours and took place on Wednesdays and Sundays. While in this state, she was unable to do anything. In the beginning the voices were female. Prior to the moment that the voices began to worsen, she had experienced some problems at a female student club. During her introduction for membership she had been confronted with sexual subjects that disturbed her. Afterwards, she was afraid that she had acted in a ridiculous manner and this resulted in her not returning to the student club. Her sensitivity towards issues of sexuality originated from her earlier life. Her mother had been a psychiatric patient and always expressed herself in a very rude and negative way about sexuality. Thus, as a child the young woman decided never to become sexually involved. Up until the time we saw her she had managed to avoid sexual relationships completely.

We made the following interpretation. The young woman could not say that the voices had any identity. We interpreted the voices as being her own mind telling herself what she was thinking. The onset of voices was connected to her confrontation with sexuality. The first episode of hearing voices occurred when she was around 14, which was also the beginning of her menstruation cycle. The second occurrence, when it began to worsen, was after she was confronted with the sexuality problem at the student club.

For this reason we decided to confront her about her decision not to deal with sexuality as we concluded that the voices were confronting her with this problem anyway. We also made this decision because she was slipping more and more into a patient role. The day after the confrontation she had sex for the first time with a boy she hardly knew. She became psychotic. We supported her, but also continued to confront her. We were able to do this because we had informed all therapists involved. After a few months she decided t change her attitude. Today she is married and she has developed into a much more independent person. She is once again in charge of herself, although every now and then she hears the voices but has developed a much more independent attitude towards them.

Conclusions
What we have shown with these examples is that the voices know the person with whom they are communicating extremely well; they usually say things that are especially relevant for the person hearing them and usually are related to their problems. The voices usually refer to an unsolved problem in daily life, and/or emotions related to a trauma that has not yet been resolved, or problems that are connected to earlier traumas or unrealized ideals that, in some cases, are impossible to realize.

In treatment, it is not relevant to reject the voices but to stimulate the curiosity of the person hearing the voices about their content. As long as the person hearing the voices reacts only in an emotional way, it will be difficult to stimulate curiosity. This is a difficult process to accomplish. One possibility is the focusing technique, as described by Bentall *et al.*, (1994). Besides focusing on characteristics of the voices, the kind of relationship that exists between the person and the voices and the possibilities of changing these relationships, it is also important to work on the problems that the person hearing voices is confronted with in their daily life.

Our experience with people hearing voices is that if the total attention in therapy is focused on treating the psychiatric illness, problems in daily life as expressed by the voices will not be solved. The final objective is not only to influence the methods used in coping with the voices but to change the manner in which he or she copes with their problems.

References

Barret, T.R. and Etheridge, J.B. (1992) 'Verbal hallucinations in Normals I: people who hear voices', Applied Cognitive Psychology 6: 379-87.

Bentall, R.P., Haddoc, G. and Slade, P.D. (1994) 'Cognitive-behaviour therapy for persistent auditory hallucinations: From theory to therapy', Behaviour Therapy 25: 51-66.

Bentall, R.P. and Slade, P.D. (1985) 'Reliability of a scale measuring disposition towards hallucinations: a brief report', Personally and Individual Differences 6: 527-9.

Eaton, W.W., Romanoski, A., Anthony, J.C. and Nestads, G. (1991) 'Screening for psychosis in the general population with a self-report interview', Journal of Nervous and Mental Disease 179: 689-93.

Ensink, B.J. (1992) Confusing Realities: a Study on Child Sexual Abuse and Psychiatric Symptoms, Amsterdam: Free University Press.

Falloon, I.R.H. and Talbot, R.E. (1981) 'Persistent auditory hallucination: coping mechanisms and implications for management', Psychological Medicine II: 329-39.

Frantz, T.T. (1984) 'Helping parents whose children have died', Family Therapy Collections 8: 11-26.

Goodwin, K. and Jamison, K.R. (1990) Manic Depressive Illness, New York: Oxford University Press.

Graham, J.R. (1987) The MMPI: A Practical Guide, 2nd edition, New York: Oxford University Press.

Landmark, J., Merkskey, Z. Cernousky, Z. and Helmes, E. (1990) 'The positive trial of schizophrenic symptoms. Its statistical properties and its relationship to thirteen traditional diagnostic systems', British Journal of Psychiatry 156: 388-94.

Posey, T.B. and Losch, M.E. (1983) 'Auditory hallucinations of hearing voices in 375 normal subjects', Imagination, Cognition and Personality 3: 99-113.

Robins, L.H., Helrer, J.E., Croughan, J. and Ratcliff, K.A. (1981) 'National Institute for Mental Health Diagnostic Interview Schedule: its history, characteristics and validity', Archives of General Psychiatry 38: 381-9.

Romme, M.A.J. and Escher, A.D.M.A.C. (1989) 'Hearing voices', Schizophrenia Bulletin 15: 209-16.

Romme, M.A.J., Honig, A., Noordhoorn, E.O., Escher, A.D.M.A.C. (1992) 'Coping with hearing voices, an emancipatory approach', British Journal of Psychiatry 16: 99-103.

Sidgewick, H.A. (1894) 'Report of the census of hallucinations', Proceedings of the Society for Psychical Research 26: 25-6.

Tien, A.Y. (1991) 'Distribution of hallucinations in the population', Social Psychiatry and Psychiatric Epidemiology 26: 287-92.

de Vries, M.W., Dijkman-Caes, C.I.M. and Delespaul, P.A.E.G. (1990) 'The Sampling of Experience, Comorbidity of Anxiety and Mood Disorders, Washington DC: Maser and Cloninger.

First published in 1996 in Dutch :
'Stemmen horen bij schizofrenie patiënten, patiënten met een dissociatieve stoornis en bij niet patiënten' in de Hert, M; Thijs E; Peuskens I; Petri D; van Raay B. in 'Zin in Waanzin, de wereld van schizofrenie' (Sense in Insanity, the world of Schizophrenia') EPO Antwerpen Belgium.

Hearing voices in patients
(Schizophrenia and dissociative disorder)
and non-patients

M.H.A. Pennings and M.A.J. Romme.

Hearing voices in patients
(Schizophrenia and dissociative disorder)
and non-patients

M.H.A. Pennings and M.A.J. Romme.

Introduction[1]

In psychiatry the basis for schizophrenia is the vulnerability-stress model, of which the vulnerability is supposedly of biological origin. The vulnerability causes the illness to become manifested under the influence of experienced stress. This model emanates from the interaction between biological vulnerability and psycho-social stress (Zubin and Spring 1977 Nuechterlein 1984; 1992, Van den Bosch 1993).

The influence of important events from the life history are not really included in this interaction. The stress is more of a trigger than part of the process in developing the illness. However, this is not the case according to the psychiatric theory about dissociative disorders. There is supposed to be a clear relationship between the experience of a series of traumatic events and the development of this disorder. In both disorders auditory hallucinations (hearing voices) occur frequently. The percentages found in the different studies to differ but are reported to be about 60% in schizophrenia (Slade and Bentall 1988, Spitzer 1988) and for dissociative disorders about 50% (Ensink 1992).[2]

It is also known that auditory hallucinations are apparent in people now showing any other sign of psycho-pathology (Posey and Losch 1983, Romme and Escher 1989, Tien 1991, Barret and Etheridge 1992). This was one of the reasons for us to do a systematic and more extensive study in three groups of people hearing voices.
- A group diagnosed as having schizophrenia
- A group diagnosed as having a dissociative disorder
- A group of non-patients.

---

[1] The research described in this chapter is a comparative study done at the University of Maastricht, department of Psychiatry, Buiks. A.M.A. Mental Health Corsten, D. MD Psychiatrist, Ensink, E. Ph.D. Psychology, Honing, A. Ph.D. Psychiatrist, Escher, A. Science Journalist, Penning, M. M.A. Health Education. The study was supervised by Prof. M. Romme Ph.D. Psychiatrist.
[2] Ensink B.E. did a study in which 100 women had experienced incest in their youth. In this group 38% developed a dissociative disorder of which 70% heard voices incidentally and 50% heard voices more regularly. Ensink (1992).

The last group were individuals who heard voices with the characteristics of auditory hallucinations, a voice heard but not produced by an observable person but with the conviction that the voices are 'not me'. These people however have never asked for psychiatric help and have never needed help in coping with their voices.

Three questions did interest us most

1. Are the formal criteria for diagnosing auditory hallucinations different between the three groups. We chose those formal criteria described by Schneider (1959) and used in the diagnostic instrument, *the present state examination* (Wing 1974), criteria that are supposed to differentiate various diagnostic categories.
2. Are there differences in the way the voices are experienced by the individuals in the different groups. Does this involve the influence of the voices on the persons behaviour and emotions.
3. Is there a difference in the interaction between the hearing of voices and the lifehistory between the three groups. A question raising interest due to the supposed difference in psychiatry in relation to schizophrenia and dissociative disorders.

Results from the study

1. The formal criteria used to differentiate between illnesses are alike in the three groups. Therefore it becomes clear, from our observed respondents anyway, that one cannot conclude the existence of a specific illness from the presence of auditory hallucinations. It needs other symptoms for diagnosing an illness.
2. The influence granted to the voices is clearly different in patients and non-patients. The content of what the voices tell the person is experienced as dominantly negative by the patient and they are also afraid of their voices. This difference in itself already differentiates the patients from the non-patients. Both patients groups do not differ from each other in this prospect.
3. In all three groups there is a connection between the initial hearing of voices experience and the experience of life events problems in that period. However, becoming a patient is related to the consequences those experienced problems have for future life, but can also be related to the circumstances during upbringing. This leads us to the conclusion that hearing voices in patients represents a social-emotional conflict that becomes internalized in the patient without an available solution in the daily life situation. This is the case in schizophrenia patients as well as in the case of dissociative disordered patients.

The interview as research instrument

We developed an interview enabling a dialogue with the voicehearers to become informed about the auditory experiences itself, the influences of the voices on the person and the interaction of these experiences with a

person's life history. This semi-structured interview covered the following subjects:
- Aspects of the experience itself
- Characteristics of the voices heard
- The life circumstances and events around the start of hearing voices
- Triggers that currently provoke the voice in daily life
- Supposed identity of the voices
- The explanation for the voices the person had adopted
- Social network, with whom the person talks to about the voices
- Experiences in childhood, including family upbringing.

The selection of the research groups
Patient groups were recruited from the Community Mental Health Centre in Maastricht (R.I.A.G.G.), department for rehabilitation, in Holland called Social Psychiatric Service. The non-patients were enrolled by advertising in the local press. Only those who actually had heard voices in the last month, with the characteristics of what is called in psychiatry an auditory hallucination, were selected. This means that other people cannot hear the voices the person involved hears those voices are experienced as 'not me' or 'ego-dystonic'. We then used a diagnostic instrument to select these persons for the different diagnostic categories. We used the C.I.D.I (Composite International Diagnostic Instrument) (Robin e.a. 1988. Wittchen e.a. 1991) and the D.E.S. (Dissociative Experiences Schedule) (Bernstein and Putnam 1986) as diagnostic instruments. Both instruments are validated in population research as well as in clinical research. They are therefore suitable for both populations with low psychopathology expectations as well populations with high psycho-pathology expectations. Three groups were composed consisting of:

- 18 patients hearing voices diagnosed according to the C.I.D.I, as having schizophrenia
- 15 patients hearing voices diagnosed with a dissociative disorder (A score of 30 or above on D.E.S., and no diagnosis of schizophrenia on the C.I.D.I.)
  15 non-patients hearing voices.

Some results:

The formal characteristics regarding the perception itself
The formal criteria that are used in psychiatric epidemiological research, for instance, the W.H.O. pilot study on schizophrenia, are assumed to differentiate between the so called 'rea;' or 'pseudo' hallucinations. The real hallucinations were seen as symptoms relating to schizophrenia. The

differentiation's between the perception of the real and pseudo hallucinations were considered to be.
1. the way the voice is heard 'by ear or in the head'
2. the experience of the voice as 'not me' or 'possibly me'
3. the ability of the person to communicate with the voices or not
4. the way the voices speak to the person in the third or second person.

According to Schneider's Symptoms of the first order, the presence of voices that talk with each other about the person (third person) or voices that comment on the behaviour of the person is sufficient for the diagnosis of schizophrenia (Schnieder 1959, Van den Bosch 1993).

	Schizophrenia N=18	Dissociative N=15	Non-Patient N=15
Hearing voices			
by ear[1]	13 (72%)	9 (60%)	7 (50%)[2]
in the head	9 (50%)	11 (73%)	10 (67%)
Ego-dystonic			
voices are me	2 (11%)	1 (7%)	3 (20%)
voices are not me	18 (100%)	14 (93%)	14 (93%)
Dialogue with voices			
can talk	12 (67%)	5 (33%)	10 (67%)
can not talk	6 (33%)	10 (67%)	5 (33%)
Being spoken to in the			
second person	17 (94%)	14 (93%)	15 (100%)
third person	7 (39%)	3 (23%)[3]	4 (27%)
commenting			
voices	13 (72%)	12 (80%)	7 (47%)

From these results it is clear that the formal characteristics of the voices do not differ between the three groups. In all three groups voices are heard by ear as well as in the head. Voices are experienced as "not me" in most cases of all groups. The possibility of communicating with the voices slightly differs between the dissociative disordered and the other two but in a controversial way because in psychiatry it is suggested that schizophrenia patients do not communicate with their voices. The last criterion also does not show the expected differences. Schizophrenics do

[1] The characteristics can be different for each voice
[2] N=14, 1 missing
[3] N=13, 2 missing

not hear the third person voices more frequently than other groups and the other groups hear commenting voices nearly as often as the schizophrenics do.

From this study it could not be confirmed that formal characteristics of auditory hallucinations do differentiate between patients and non-patients. Therefore one should not diagnose a specific illness from the presence of auditory hallucinations only.

The influence of the voices on the person's emotions and behaviour
People hearing voices differ from each other as far as the influence of the voices on their emotions and behaviour is concerned. This influence can also be different for each voice heard. Most people hear positive as well as negative voices, but the overall effect and the supposed consequences might be different. This was the reason to ask the person for positive voices and what they told the person, as well as for negative voices and what those told the person. Subsequently we asked about the effect of these texts on the person's behaviour and emotions. We then inquired, as a kind of concluding question, whether the voices were experienced as predominantly positive, negative or neutral.

The following questions were then asked:
- whether this made the person afraid for the voices
- whether they were upset by them or
- whether the experience was disturbing their daily functioning.

	Schizophrenic N=18	Dissociative N=15	Non-patients N=15
positive voices	15 (83%)	10 (67%)	14 (93%)
negative voices	18 (100%)	14 (93%)	10 (67%)
predominantly positive	2 (11%)	2 (13%)	11 (79%)[1]
neutral	4 (22%)	3 (20%)	3 (21%)[1]
predominantly negative	12 (67%)	10 (67%)	nobody [1]
afraid of the voices:	14 (78%)	11 (84%)[2]	nobody [1]
upset by the voices:	16 (89%)	13 (100%)[2]	4 (27%)
disturbing daily life	18 (100%)	14 (100%)[1]	5 (33%)

[1] N=14, 1 missing
[2] N=13, 2 missing

This graph shows first of all a conformity between the three groups: patients as well as non-patients hear positive as well as negative voices.

The main differences between patients and non-patients however are: the patient groups experience the voices as dominantly negative, while the non-patient groups experience the voices as dominantly positive. Another difference is that the patient groups are afraid of the voices which is not the case with the non-patient group. The third difference is that the patient groups are disturbed by the voices in the performance of their daily activities while this is much less the case in the non-patients. The two patient groups do not differ from each other, they are both afraid of the voices, are disturbed by them in the performance of their daily activities and experience the voices as dominantly negative or threatening.

The influence of the person hearing voices has on the voices
The voices exercise their influence on the person and the other side of this interaction is the influence of the voice hearer on the voices. Questions asked in the interview, for instance. Do you have control over the voices, Can you refuse orders given by the voices and Do voices make you powerless.

	Schizophrenia N=18	Dissociative N=15	Non-patients N=15
has control over the voices	3 (17%)	1 (7%)	13 (87%)
voices make the person powerless	13 (72%)	10 (71%)	2 (13%)
can refuse orders given by the voices	16 (89%)	10 (67%)	15 (100%)

In this table we see considerable differences in the experience of their control over the voices between patients and non-patient. Nearly all non-patients feel that they are in control (83%). However, this is not the case in the patient groups. Only 17% of the schizophrenia patients and only 7% of the dissociative disordered patients feel that they themselves are in control. Both patient groups also feel powerless towards their voices in over 70% of the respondents while the non-patients do not experience powerlessness in 87%. The feeling of powerlessness in patients is not caused by their inability to refuse orders. On the contrary, a high percentage in both patient groups say that they can refuse orders.

The feeling of powerlessness in patients is most likely related to the life history and what has happened in their lives. They have a feeling of powerlessness over the traumatic events and experienced circumstances. They experience this same emotion with the voices.

Hearing voices and the life history

We held our first inquiry amongst people hearing voices in 1987. As a result, 70% talked about a traumatic event which they could relate to the voice hearing experience (Romme and Escher 1989: 1993) From a study by Ensink (1992) 100 women who became patients in later life associated hearing voices to incest experiences in their youth. Ensink studied the psycho-pathology in these women and found a high percentage of auditory hallucinations (appr.50%) In this comparative study of patients and non-patients we tried to be more specific about the relation between the voices hearing experience and events in the life history. We differentiated information about the life history. We asked about what had happened around the time the person heard voices for the first time and, separately in another part of the interview, about what had happened during the younger years during upbringing in and outside the family. We also informed ourselves about the life history following the start of the voices. From this information we can conclude that hearing voices and becoming a patient are not related to the same origin or causes. We were able to study this differentiation because we also studied non-patients hearing voices.

The relation between voices and life history will be reported on group level and illustrated with some case-examples. In the next table we mention external circumstances, events or changes with which according to the voices nearer the start of hearing voices is connected. These concerns realities in daily life that are emotionally negatively experienced and could therefore be called stresses. These stresses however can not be defined only as psychological but represent real interaction or changes in life in which others play an important role. The table shows that in our respondent groups 77% of the schizophrenic patients and 100% of the dissociative disordered patients have experienced such circumstances. But also half of the non-patients associate such influences from their life history with the start of their hearing voices.

Schizophrenic N=18	Dissociative N=15	Non-patients N=15
Clear circumstances at the beginning		
13 (77%)	15 (100%)	8 (53%)

*   Loss of a dear one (by means of suicide)
*   Go and live on ones own

* Breaking off a relationship
* Severe stress within the family
* Unwanted sexual identity confrontation
* Physical abuse/assault
* Sexual abuse/assault
* Severe illness

These social stresses however got their significance only within the personal history of the respondents life. A traumatic event for instance can have consequences for the future life but does not have to. The consequences can be positive or negative. This differs with the character of the trauma, with the experienced power or powerlessness to overcome the trauma and with the defensibility of the person who encounters the trauma. The power or powerlessness experienced over the trauma will influence the power given to the voices and the power taken by the voices in a persons perception. This will influence a persons emotions and behaviour towards the voices. Those who remain powerless after the trauma will be powerless against the voices and those who are made less powerless by the traumatic events will be more defensive towards the voices. But there are many more influences as far as defensibility is concerned.

The 48 life-histories
From the 48 life-histories, we have learned that we have to differentiate between the reasons for hearing voices and the reason for becoming a patient. Circumstance that evoke the hearing of voices might be described as existential trauma's that is to say events by which a person feels threatened in the continuity of his existence. These events took place shortly before the voices were heard for the first time.

In the following case-examples we describe three case-histories and differentiate the information of the existential trauma related to the beginning of hearing voices from the information on the life-history, in our view linked to becoming a patient or not.

A few examples might illustrate this interaction
An example of a patient diagnosed as dissociative disordered;
- A nine year old girl has been beaten so severely by her father, that she has to be admitted to hospital because two vertebra have been dislocated. Two hour after admission she heard voices for the first time.

Physically the girl recovered completely and was placed in her grandmothers care, which was very nice and gave her a safe surrounding. So at first, there were no negative consequences for her connected with the trauma. However, three years later her grandmother died and she was then admitted into an institute. In this institute there was no more security, similar to her fathers' house. In this institute education and well behaviour were aggressively forced upon her and she probably was more sensitive to that behaviour. Anyhow, she became too vulnerable in order to cope with the voices.

An example of a patient diagnosed as having schizophrenia;

-   A forty year old man starts hearing voices a few days before he has to do an examination that is vital to keep his job, when he realizes that he will certainly fail because the requirements are to heavy for him.

In his life this trauma has been like a repetition. He as vulnerable and could not cope due to the fact that he has been belittled by his father in his youth and so had been labelled as stupid. This resulted in his brother being given the fathers' farm and he had to look for a profession elsewhere which now he was scared he would lose.

An example of a non-patient hearing voices;

-   A forty year old woman starts hearing voices after the loss of three very important people in her life, her husband, her father and her sister in law, all dying within a period of three months.

She did not become a patient. The loss of her dear ones as an emotional trauma, but it did not being negative consequences into her life. She did not have to change her daily life neither financially nor did she have to change housing or lose her children. Furthermore her history showed a childhood and education in which she was very much stimulated and supported. She developed a stable identity and was not that vulnerable when she suffered the losses.

The events evoking the hearing of voices according to our interpretation are threatening because; **the event**

1. is threatening similar to sever ill-treatment or illness.
2. is threatening because it threatens the continuity of ones expectations in the case of losing ones job; a divorce, or death of a dear one.
3. is threatening because of an overwhelming emotional confrontation like the death of the father who abused the person or the confrontation with a not accepted sexual identity.

The big difference according to our interpretation, between those who become a patient due to hearing voices ad those who did not seem to be;

1   The different consequences the traumatic event has on ones life. For instance, one can be cured completely from a life threatening illness but can also remain seriously handicapped.
2. The difference in defensibility and identity formation build up during the lifetime before the trauma happened. This seems to be important in overcoming a traumatic or series of traumatic events.

Conclusion

The above mentioned results from analysing the life-history, in relation to the hearing voices experience and coping abilities, show that the problem is not that hearing voices is called a psychotic phenomenon but the problem seem to be that in psychiatric care psychotic phenomena are differently treated in comparison or relation between neurotic symptoms and life history has been accepted and plays a role in diagnosis and treatment.

There are many reasons why in psychotic phenomena psychiatry has accentuated a different view but that is not our point here. We would like to emphasize that psychotic phenomena can be understood from the personal life-history. Not because we are embarking on a new subject, but because we encountered the problem from another angle, the comparison of patients and non-patients both hearing voices and both having suffered traumatic events.

We also would like to stress that it is possible for a person to understand his or her psychotic reactions, because we have met several patients who learned to understand their psychotic reactions and could integrate them in their life and could step our of the patient role. Although one's history remains the same, the consequences for future life can be changed. Understanding voices by the person who hears them can influence their coping and problems solving. This might be a possibility in continuing ones development and take one life in one's own hands again. This by no means is invariably successful. It takes quite some courage since a different way of coping with problems in daily life can be very threatening.

The study we described in this chapter also made us realize that psychiatric diagnosis can become a handicap for a patient. This is also not new, but we have addressed this problem by looking at healthy people with a psychotic phenomenon.

All of us know, but have not so eloquently argumented this reality, unlike van Praag (1986 - 1992) and Bentall (1988 - 1992), that schizophrenia is a circum script diagnostic category still misses scientific validity. It is rather difficult though to listen to those messages as long as one does not know what to do else. We would like to propose, following our own observations, a possible alternative given that the general psychiatric diagnosing process encloses a danger, making patients powerless in influencing their health. Diagnosing illness-entities is based on the sequence that symptoms are consequences of the illness. Therefore in the psychiatric separate symptoms, nor in the interaction between symptoms, Another consequence from this process is that the psychiatrist does not explore the relation between symptoms and life-history and nor is the interaction between symptoms explored. From our observation it could quite well be possible that the sequence of cause and consequence could also be the reverse of what is thought of in the Kraepelinian concept.

Anyhow in a number of cases it is possible that hearing voices represents a social-emotional problem that is really difficult to handle for the person and therefore makes it less easy to cope with the voices. This is a reason to feel powerless against the voices and also against the problem involved. We than see a series of secondary reactions like concentration disturbances, inadequate affect outbursts; social isolating behaviour; and other behaviours that are incomprehensible for the near family because they represent for instance rituals that prevent one self from doing what the voices order one to do. It could be that in those cases the voices are not the consequence of the underlying illness but that the illness becomes the consequence of the way one copes with the voices.

References

Barrett, T.R., en J.B. Etheridge (1992), Verbal Hallucinations in Normals I: People who hear 'Voices'. *Applied Cognitive Psychology*, 6, 379-387.

Benthall, R.P., H.F. Jackson en D. Pilgrim (1988), Abandoning the concept of 'schizophrenia': some implications of validity arguments for psychological research into psychotic phenomena. *British Journal of Clinical Psychology* 27, 303-324.

Benthall, R.P. (ed.) (1990), *Reconstructing schizophrenia*. Routledge London/New York.

Bernstein, E.M., en F.W. Putman (1986), Development, reliability and validity of a dissociation scale. *Journal of Nervous and Mental Disease* 174, 727-735

Bleuler, E. (1983), *Lehrbuch der Psychiatrie*. Springer-Verlag, Berlijn.

Bosch van den, R.J. (1990), Schizofrenie en andere functionele psychotische stoornissen. In: W. Vandereyken, C.A.L. Hoogduin en P.M.G. Emmelkamp (red.), *Handboek psychopathologie, deel 1*. Bohn Stafleu Van Loghum,, Houten/Antwerpen.

Bosch van den, R.J. (1993), *Schizofrenie: subjectieve ervaringen en cognitief onderzoek*. Bohn Stafleu Van Loghum, Houten.

Ensink, B.J. (1992), *Confusing realities: a study on child sexual abuse and psychiatric symptoms*. VU University Press, Amsterdam.

Ensink, B.J. (1994), *Psychiatrische klachten na een misbruikverleden. Een onderzoek onder honderd vrouwen*. Maanblad Geestelijke Volksgezondheid, 4, 387-404.

Falloon, I.R.H., en R.E. Talbot (1981), Persistent auditory hallucinations: coping mechanisms and implications for management, *Psychological Medicines*, 11, 329-339.

Gelder, M., D. Gath en R. Mayou (1991), *Oxford Textbook of Psychiatry*. Oxford University Press. Oxford

Kaplan, H.I., en B.J. Saddock (1989), *Comprehensive Textbook of Psychiatry*. Williams & Willins, Baltimore.

Neuchterlein, K.H., en M.E. Dawson (1984). A heuristic vulnerability/ stress model of schizophrenic episodes. *Schizophrenia Bulletin*, 10, 300-312.

Neuchterlein, K.H., M.E. Dawson en M. Gitlin e.a. (1992), Developmental Processes in Schizophrenic Disorders; longitudinal study of vulnerability and stress, *Schizophrenia Bulletin*, 18, 387-425.

Posey, T.B., en Losch (1983), auditory hallucinations of hearing voices in 375 normal subjects *Imagination, Cognition and Personality*, 3 (2) 99-113.

Praag, van H.M. (1992) *Make Believes in Psychiatry or The Perils of Progress*. Brunner/Mazel, New York.

Robins, L.N., J. Wing, H.U. Wittchen e.a. (1988) The Composite International Diagnostic Interview. *Arch Gen. Psychiatry*, 45. 1069-1077.

Romme, M.A.J. en A.D.M.A.C. Escher (1989), hearing voices *Schizophrenia Bulletin*, 15 (2), 209-216.

Romme, M.A.J. en A.D.M.A.C. Escher (1993), *Accepting voices*. Mind Publication, London.

Schneider, K. (1959), *Clinical Psychopathology*. 5e editie, Grune & Stratton, New York.

Slade. P.D. en R.P. Bentall (1988) *Sensory deception*, Croom Helm Ltd, London.

Spitzer, M. (1988), *Halluzinationen; ein Beitrag zur allgemeinen und klinischen Psychopathologie*. Springer Verlag, Berlin.

Tien, A.Y. (1991), Distribution of hallucinations in the population. *Social Psychiatry and Psychiatric Epidemiology*, 26, 287-292

Wing. J.K., J.E. Cooper en N. Satorius (1974), The measurement and classification of psychiatric symptoms. Cambridge University Press. Cambridge/New York.

Wittchen, H.U., L.N. Robins, L.B. Cottler e.a. (1991), Cross-cultural Feasibility, Reliability and sources of Variance of the Composite International diagnostic Interview (CIDI) *British Journal of Psychiatry*, 159, 645-653

Zubin, J., en B. Spring (1977), Vulnerability: a new way of schizophrenia. *Journal of Abnormal Psychology*, 86, 103-126.

Concluding Remarks

Marius Romme

The first important result of our experiment was meeting socially well functioning people who had never been psychiatric patients but heard voices with the same characteristics as auditory hallucinations in patients. They also heard voices while no-body was there and were also convinced of the 'not-me' quality of those voices.

We realized that it is very difficult for psychiatrists to accept the existence of non-patients. This is comprehensible because psychiatrists do not meet people who do not need psychiatric care. Secondly psychiatrists are trained to interpret hearing voices as a symptom of a mental illness. This is reinforced because they only meet people who cannot cope with their voices. Thirdly, there is an intense taboo in our society about having such experiences. Even the psychiatrists we encountered who hear voices themselves do not communicate about their experience except with people they know very well and feel safe with.

The acceptance that there are healthy people hearing voices with the characteristics of auditory hallucinations is a prerequisite to change one's view that it is not the experience itself that is a sign of mental illness but that the way of coping with this experience may lead to or can be the expression of mental illness.

Therefore the target of the treatment should not be aimed directly at curing or eliminating the experience itself but by helping with the coping process. The coping process is the psychological process between one's perception and one's reactions. A direct attack on the voices means neglecting the coping process but trying to suppress the perception. The second important result of our studies was that in most cases hearing voices can be made comprehensible from the persons life history and experiences. The relationship between traumatic experiences and the onset of hearing voices made it clear that the coping process can be a difficult issue.

There are many possible reasons for this. One reason might be that the person cannot handle the original trauma or life situation in which the voices started. Another reason is the believe system developed by the person. Different studies show that the interpretation of the voices, like the voice of the devil or the voice of a good guide, does influence the effect of the voices (Nijhof, 1990 Chadwick et al 1994). The coping difficulty can also be influenced by the catastrophically believe in society that hearing voices is a sign of a serious mental illness as described by Kingdon and Turkington (1994).

The coping can also be negatively influenced because of the emotions provoked by the voices for which adequate coping strategies are lacking. Coping strategy enhancement is one of the possibilities described by Yusupoff and Tarrier (1996).

Another reason for failing to cope might be that people who hear voices as well as their family and doctors do not focus on the experience in relation to the life situation and emotions provoking them. This is described by Haddock et al (1996). These different elements influence the ability to cope.

The third and perhaps the most important result of our studies is that hearing voices is an individual reaction on personal problems or ideals which also leads to a very individual sequence of emotions and behaviours or reaction pattern which might mimic the symptoms of different mental illnesses as categorized in psychiatry.

The individuality of the experience is expressed by the content of the voices which metaphorically expresses the trouble people are having with their emotions reflecting confusing experiences ideals or the lack of certain capacities like making decisions on one's own in daily life.

Non of the experiences are alike in the sense that what the voices tells them differs per person and refers to different histories.

There does not seem to be a general cause neither for the perception itself neither for the reaction pattern. The whole pattern of interactions is very personal and perhaps also explaining why there is such a difference in symptoms within psychotic disorders. This could explain why patients even diagnosed with a particular psychotic disorder differ so much in symptoms patterns.

It might be that the greatest handicap to develop more knowledge about psychotic disorders is our obsessive search for general causes, trying to explain the different behaviour patterns from one cause. This search is possibly related to the believe that circumscript psychotic illnesses are available although we know that this is not a scientific validated reality.

We like to look for causes in the brain or in the psycho-social influences to explain the development of illness entities. But what if this does not exist and people just react in different ways because their experiences are different.

They still can be perceived as psychotic disordered but they can only be helped by translating the reaction pattern into an understandable process. This individual approach was the basis for the interview we developed to understand the individual variations in perception and interaction related to the life history.

We learnt from our case studies that solving problems in daily life may have positive influences in the coping with voices. In the same period psychological research groups in England developed individual oriented intervention techniques accentuating different aspects of the coping process.

All this leaves us with a very important research question concerning interventions:

Do the cognitive behavioral interventions that are focused on the perception itself and the coping with that perception have sufficient influence on a person solving his/her problems in daily life. Or is it necessary that the person also is helped by solving those problems in order to overcome their dependency of the voices. The next examples will illustrate the problem involved.

We met two young men, who both heard voices and who both had trouble accepting their homosexual tendencies and they where both patients. The therapist of one of them asked us how to interpret the voices. We asked the therapist to do the interview and we analyzed the data, indicating that the voices pointed to a problem with sexuality, probably homosexuality. This therapist helped the person to learn to know his voices better and gradually accepting his homosexuality. This made it possible for him to develop his identity.

The other man told his parents when he was 17 years old that he was homosexual. His parents transformed this message into an other view 'that he was sexually misused in bars where he, still rather young, accidentally went to' They felt responsible for his well-being and took very nice care of him. At the age of 29 he still lives with his parents. He gradually developed more and more negative symptoms with aggressive outbursts towards his parents. He is now diagnosed Schizophrenia. He did not develop a homosexual identity but is more perceived as still rather childish.

Now we do not think that homosexuality causes Schizophrenia but only that a dilemma, which a person cannot avoid, can be a reason for hearing voices. Failing to solve this dilemma can lead to more 'illness behaviour'. Solving the dilemma leads to less stress and less risk of developing more illness behaviour.

In our case studies it became evident that identity development is an important issue in this process. In order to cope with voices and to overcome confusing problems, it is important to be able to be allowed to develop one's own identity, making choices, solving dilemma's.

Understanding the voices is necessary in order to get insight into ones problems. If they can be solved, the specific personal stress will diminish as well as the risk for psychotic decompensation.

Cognitive interventions are necessary to gain more control over the voices but this might be only half way towards well-being. Prevention of psychotic decompensation was possible in a number of our cases by cognitive strategies but requires continuity of care. We also got to know people who were able to solve their problems or could take another point of view towards them. Those people impressed us because they became self-supporting and the preventive effect was lasting. This process is well described by Ron Coleman (1995), Anonymous (1993) Babs Johnston (1995) and Parker et al (1995).

Psychiatry should realize that a lot of people who hear voices never visit a psychiatrist or psychiatric service because they develop their own way of coping and solve their own problems. While those who ask for help in psychiatry are diagnosed with an illness and treated accordingly. They are not sufficiently helped with their specific personal problems.

The psychiatric idea that the illness is inherited and is only triggered by the stress or trauma might still be true. It is only a pity when psychiatric care should conclude that the person cannot be helped otherwise than by suppressing the psychotic symptoms.

A pity because we have met cases who changed their attitude towards their voices and towards their problems and could take their own life in their own hands again. Voice hearers, family and society could profit from such changes.

References

Nijhoff G. 91990) over autobiografische verklaringen van stemmen horen (about autobiographical explanations of hearing voices) 36-53 in Romme M. & Escher A., Stemmen horen accepteren Maastricht.

Chadwick P.D.J. and Birchwood M.J. (1994) Challenging the omnipotence of voices. A cognitive approach to auditory hallucinations, British Journal of Psychiatry 164: 190-201.

Kingdom D.G. and Turkington D. (1994) Cognitive Behavioral, Therapy of schizophrenia, Lawrence Erlbaum Associates Publishers Hove U.K.

Yusopoff and Terrier N. (1996) Coping strategy, Enchancement for persistent hallucinations and Delusions, 86-103 in Haddock G and Slade P., Cognitive Behavioural Interventions with Psychotic disorders, Routledge London.

Haddock, G., bentall R.P. and Slade P (1986), Psychological treatment and Auditory Hallucinations Focussing or distraction 45-71 in: Haddock G. and Slade P., Cognitive Behavioural Interventions with Psychotic Disorders, Routledge London.

Coleman, R. (1995). Wij zijn lang genoeg slachtoffer geweest (From victim to owner) Deviant 2; 12-13, Amsterdam, Holland.

Anonymous (1993), Growing out of psychiatry, Twelfth Contribution page 140-145 in Romme M. and Escher A., Accepting Voices, Mind London.

Johnston, B. (1995), Self-help and relationship, Newcastle, U.K.

Parker I; Georgaca E; Harper D; McLaugklin T; Stowell-smith M (1005) Deconstructing Psychopathology, Sage Publications London.

Maastricht interview [1]
with
a voice hearer

Sandra Escher, Patsy Hage, Marius Romme

Introduction for voice hearers:
We asked you to cooperate in our research project because you told us
that you hear voices. You are an experienced expert and possess knowledge concerning these special experiences. Therefore, we could like to
ask you to share this knowledge with us. The meaning of this interview is
to achieve a better understanding of these experiences. Among other things
we would like to know in what circumstances these voices present themselves and we would like to draw up an inventory of the methods you use
in order to cope with these voices. Perhaps you have devised a method
that enables you to overpower the voices and if so, is it possible to teach
others to do the same?

Since this interview is very extensive, it is possible that you may
wish to conduct it in two sessions rather than one. Please feel free to let
us know when you are getting tired and we will reschedule a new ap-
pointment. Should any clarification be needed once the interview has been
completed, we would like to have your permission to contact you. In the
interest of conducting a proper and valid research project it is important
that we get all the facts correct.

---

[1] This interview has been used during our research. This concised version is currently used in therapy. Following a pilot study the original interview designed by
the authors, was refined by M.H.A. Pennings.

1. ASPECTS OF THE EXPERIENCES ITSELF

This interview is meant as a dialogue about your experience. You are an expert. You own your experiences. This interview will enable us to learn more about your experience and the way you cope with your voices.

1.1 I would like you to give me a broad view of any extraordinary experiences you have had recently or in the past.

....

....

1.2 How many voices do you hear? At what age did you first hear voices?

....

....

number of voices ( ) now ( ) at the start
age at the beginning ( ) years

1.3 Can these sounds/voices also be heard by other people? Yes/no
Can you explain why?

....

....

1.4 Where do you hear the voice(s) (location)?

	now	at the beginning
In your head	yes/no	yes/no
Through your ears (left/right/both)	yes/no	yes/no
somewhere else within your body	yes/no	yes/no
The voices appear to come from somewhere outside the body	yes/no	yes/no

1.5 Concerning the voices you hear:
Are these voices coming from your own person or are they from somebody else?
(The point we are trying to establish here is now somebody experiences the voices at the moment of perception.)

The voices are coming out of
my own person *(ego-syntonic/me)* yes/no
The voices are coming from somebody or something outside of my person *(ego-syntonic/not me)* yes/no
Can you explain why?

....

....

58

1.6   Are you able to carry on a dialogue with the voices or communicate in any way with them?   yes/no
Give an example:

....

....

To be concluded by the interviewer:
Does the hearing of voices possess the same or similar characteristics as an **auditory hallucination**
1. The respondent can hear voices that others cannot hear   yes/no
2. The respondent hears voices through the ears   yes/no
3. The respondent hears voices in his/her head   yes/no
4. The respondent is able to maintain a dialogue   yes/no
    or other method of communication
5. The voices are experienced as me (1) or not-me (2)   1 / 2

---

2.   CHARACTERISTICS OF THE VOICES

2.1   Do you hear one or more voices? How many? Has it always been like this?
Has the number of voices ever changed?

....

....

	now	**at the beginning**
Number of voices heard now	[ ]	[ ]

2.2   Are you able to indicate who the voices are or which names you have given to the voices.

no	name	age	gender	contents/tone	frequency
1					
2					
3					
4					
5					

2.3   Does the manner or tone of the voices remind you of someone you know or knew? If yes, who?

....

....

3. THE HISTORY OF HEARING VOICES

3.1 Let us go back to the start. When did you first begin hearing voices? (age) .... years. How many years, months, have you been hearing voices?

....

....

3.2 Can you describe for every voice the circumstances you first heard them?

....

....

3.3 Circumstances related to the beginning
Other voice hearers told us they started to hear voices after a live event.
I will give you some examples other voice hearers told us. Do you recognize one of the circumstances as happening to you?
At what age did this happen?   *(note: follow the list)*

yes/ no	circumstances	age and year
	The result of a serious physical damage or serious illness	
	An admission to a hospital or being put under narcosis	
	Living on you own for the first time	
	Following: a divorce or breaking up an intimate relation	
	a pregnancy/abortion or the first menstruation	
	a major decline in the health situation of a loved one	
	admission to a psychiatric hospital	
	employment changes (starting work, promotion)	
	employment set backs retirement/unable to work	
	After: the death of a close friend or family member	
	beginning with a course study	
	you found yourself unemployed/fired/business closed	
	you had fell in love and been rejected	
	a move to a new residence or school	
	problems within a religious circle/ sectarian society	
	influential circumstance f.e. seances, satanic church	
	when confronted with a present at a suicide	
	during severe tension in your home or your relationship	
	when a child left the house/ last child left the house	

3.4 Does one or more of this circumstances are related to the fact you began to hear voices? If so, could you describe how?

....

....

4. TRIGGERS
4.1 Have you noticed that the voices are present under particular circumstances or activities? Can you describe what these are?

....

....

4.2 Did you notice that the voices are present when you feel certain emotions?
Let us check this list: You are experiencing emotions such as:

[ ] insecurity   [ ] jealousy
[ ] fear   [ ] grief
[ ] doubt   [ ] fatigue
[ ] in love   [ ] depressed or sad
[ ] anger or aggression   [ ] happy
[ ] your own sexual feelings   [ ] lonely
[ ] the sexual feelings of others

Can you describe how the voices react? (confort; help; make the feeling stronger or less present?) Can you give an example?

....

....

5. CONTENTS OF THE VOICES
5.1 Do you hear positive (friendly) voices? What do they say; what do they do? Give an example.

....

....

5.2 Do you hear negative (unfriendly) voices? What do they say; what do they do? Give an example.

....

....

5.3 Do the voices talk about specific subjects/persons? Can you describe them? What do the voices say? Do those subjects have your interest as well?

....

....

6. INFLUENCE OF THE VOICES

We would like to ask you what kind of influence the voices have?

6.3 Are you afraid of the voices? Why? Have you always been afraid? Please give an example.

....

....

6.4 Do the voices upset you? How do they do this? Please give an example.

....

....

6.5 Do the voices disturb your daily activities? How do they do that? Please give an example.

....

....

6.6 Do the voices confuse you? How do they do that? Please give an example.

....

....

6.7 How do you experience the voices as:

	now	**at the beginning**
predominately positive voices	yes/no	yes/no
predominately negative voices	yes/no	yes/no
neutral	yes/no	yes/no
negative as well as positive	yes/no	yes/no

7. ORIGIN OF THE VOICES/INTERPRETATION

As a voice hearer you want an explanation for origin of the voices, as professionals do. However, often you do not have the same frame of references. I want to discuss the origin and it concerns two aspects. The identification; who is the voice and the frame of reference. I would like to know what your ideas are about both. I want to discuss the identification first.

6.1 Which identify do you give the voices? This is about perception, who do you think they are?

The voices are from a living person:

1. who is part of your daily life	yes/no
2. your parents or another family member	yes/no
3. who is unknown to you	yes/no

The voices are from a deceased person:

4. who was very well known to you	yes/no
5. who was unknown to you	yes/no

The voices are:

6. symptoms of an illness	yes/no

7. one or more parts of your personality
   (from the unconsciousness)   yes/no

The voices are:
   8. a good guide   yes/no
   9. a ghost from somcone our of the past (reincarnation)   yes/no
   10. gods, ghosts or angels   yes/no
   11. a good god   yes/no
   12. a bad spirit or the devil   yes/no
   13. entities (a spiritual person or power that you cannot
       see but is there. You feel or hear the presencc of it)   yes/no
   14. extraordinary perceptions (telepathy, mediumistic)   yes/no
   15. result from the pain of others or from something
       else around you   yes/no

Please describe in which theoretical frame of reference you think
your experience relates to and why.

....

....

7.3   Do the voices each have a different frame of reference? If yes why?

....

....

8.   RELATIONSHIP WITH THE VOICES

We would like to ask you what kind of relationship you have with
the voices.

8.1   Are you able to influence the voice in any way?   yes/no
      Please give an example.

....

....

8.2   Do the voices leave you powerless? If yes, how do they accomplish
      this? (by their presence or by what they say?)

....

....

8.3   Are you in control of the voices? Has this always been so? Please
      describe.

....

....

8.4   Are you able to talk with the voices? Do you do this? Do you speak
      out loud or do you speak in your mind? (or both) How do the voices
      react. Have they always reacted in this way? If not, why?

Please give an example.

....

....

8.5 Do you ever call the voices names? If yes, how? Do you do that out loud or in your mind? Are you able to recall the voices?

....

....

8.6 Are you able to refuse orders? If yes, which orders can you refuse and which not? What happens if you refuse to do what the voices order?

....

....

8.7 Are you able to cut yourself off from the voices and to open up again?

....

....

8.8 If you hear voices do you mainly concentrate on what the voices say or on what you are doing? Does this differ per voice or per moment?

....

....

9.10.11. COPING STRATEGIES

We have just discussed your relationship with the voices. I would like to know what exactly you do, when you hear the voices. *If the answer is yes, please ask how many times and what the effect is.*
What do you do when you hear voices?

9. COGNITIVE STRATEGIES

no	strategy	yes/no	if yes, describe
1	send the voice away		
2	ignore the voices		
3	concentrate on listening		
4	selective listening pattern		
5	forcing your thoughts in another direction		
6	make a deal with the voice		
7	do you sometimes limit the voices		

10. BEHAVIOURAL STRATEGIES

no	strategy	yes/no	if yes, describe
8	do you start to do something		
9	fly for the voices		
10	telephone		
11	to visit someone		
12	distract yourself		
13	keep a diary about the voices		
14	certain behaviour or rituals		

11. PHYSIOLOGICAL STRATEGIES

no	strategy	yes/no	if yes, describe
15	relaxation exercises such as yoga		
16	medication		
17	alcohol and drugs		
18	food		

CONCLUSION COPING STRATEGIES

12.1 What method do you use most? How often do you use it? Do you use it systemically? If no, why not?

....

....

12.2 What is the result (less power or do you gain additional power)?

....

....

12.3 If you know that in certain circumstances the voices appear, do you seek a different approach? (alternative, avoiding, try not to be influenced)

....

....

12.4 In the past, have you ever tried something that seemed to help?

....

....

10. QUESTIONS RELATED TO YOUR CHILDHOOD

Childhood can be a very different experience for people. Some people like to look back while other prefer to put it behind them as soon as possible. What is your perception of your childhood?

10.1 Was your childhood stressful or pleasant? Can you tell me about it?

....

....

10.2 Did you feel safe at school, in the streets and at home? If not, please explain why?

....

....

10.3 As a child, have you ever been mistreated? How?

....

....

10.4 As a child, did you ever receive strange punishment? For example, being locked in a toilet or being tied up?

....

....

10.5 Have you ever, as a child or a teenager, been yelled at or belittled? Did you experience the feeling of not being wanted, or did you feel that you were never able to do anything right?

....

....

10.6 Have you ever witnessed the maltreatment of another family member?

....

....

10.7 Have you ever been sexually abused by a member of the family?

....

....

10.8 Have you ever had sex against your will? A situation where you were unable to resist or escape from?

....

....

11. MEDICAL HISTORY

11.1 Did you ever get therapy? Did you ever get therapy because of the voices? Which kind of therapist?

year	clinic/ambulant	kind of therapist	lengths	indication for treatment

11.2 With which therapist did you talk about the voices ?

....

....

11.3 What did the therapist do in relation to the voices?

....

....

12. SOCIAL NETWORK

Contact with others is an important part of life. First I would like to ask you to tell me about the person with whom you have a personal relationship and other persons that are important to you. The order is not important and you are not required to give complete names. Initials or something like 'my son' is sufficient.

RESPONSE FILE SOCIAL NETWORK

NO	NAME	knows about the voices yes/no	talks about the voices yes/no
01			
02			
03			
04			
05			
06			
07			
08			

Main Publications

Romme M.A.J.; Escher A.D.M.   1989 Hearing Voices
                               Schizophrenia Bulletin
                               Vol. 15 (2) 209-216

Romme M.A.J.; Honig A.   1992. Coping with hearing
Noorthoorn E.O;   voices, an emancipatory
Escher A.D.M.   approach.
                               British Journal of Psychiatry
                               16: 99-103.

Romme M.A.J.; Escher A.D.M.   1993. Accepting Voices
                               Mind Publications London

Romme M.A.J.; Escher A.D.M.   1996. Empowering People who
                               hear voices in Haddock G. and Slade
                               P. Cognitive Behaviour Intervention
                               with Psychotic Disorders.
                               Routledge, London.

Pennings M.H.J.; Romme M.A.J. Auditieve Hallucinaties bij patiënten
                               en niet patiënten.
                               Ned. tijdschrift voor Psychiatrie
                               Accepted June 1996

Pennings M.H.J.; Romme M.A.J. Stemmen horen bij Schizofrenie
                               patiënten, patiënten met een
                               dissociatieve stoornis en niet-
                               patiënten, in: M. de Hert et all
                               Zin in Waanzin
                               De wereld van Schizofrenie
                               EPO Antwerpen België